Play and Learn with Numbers

This Play and Learn book is suitable for 3-5 year ⟨...⟩ introduce children to numbers in a fun filled way. Most children will need a little help with some of the pages. Once you have shown them what they have to do leave them to complete the page. There are lively, familiar illustrations for all the activities. The educational content of each activity links home learning with school.

This workbook encourages children to understand and enjoy numbers. The answers can be found at the back of the book.

Play and Learn with Numbers contains:

- **Simple counting** - Children learn to count up to ten in the correct order.
- **Counting rhymes** - An activity children enjoy. Simple rhymes to learn and count.
- **Add and take away** - They learn the difference between adding and taking away numbers.
- **Number mazes and trails** - Counting in the correct order leads the children through the mazes and along the trails to find the correct answers.
- **Colour by numbers** - Children are encouraged to learn five different colours, how to recognise them by numbers and complete the pictures.
- **Dot-to-dot** - Simple dot-to-dot puzzles. Children complete the pictures by counting in the right order from one to ten.
- **Time** - Encourages children to write in the correct time by using picture recognition.

1 2 3 4

5 6 7

8 9 10

How many bears in the picture? Trace over the right number.

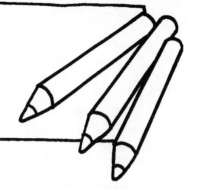

Two little bears one white and one brown
One with a smile one with a frown
Don't be sad come home with me
Said the bear with a smile and have some tea

1 2 3

Colour the fish and tick
the smallest number.

Colour and count the number of stripes on the snake.

stripes

Join up the dots to find
who is in the picture.

Colour boat number 7 blue, boat number 2 yellow and boat number 4 green.

Fill in the missing numbers.

1 2 3 4 5

6 7 8 9 10

Colour in the pictures.
Draw a ring round the
odd one out.

Add the fish and write
down the answers.

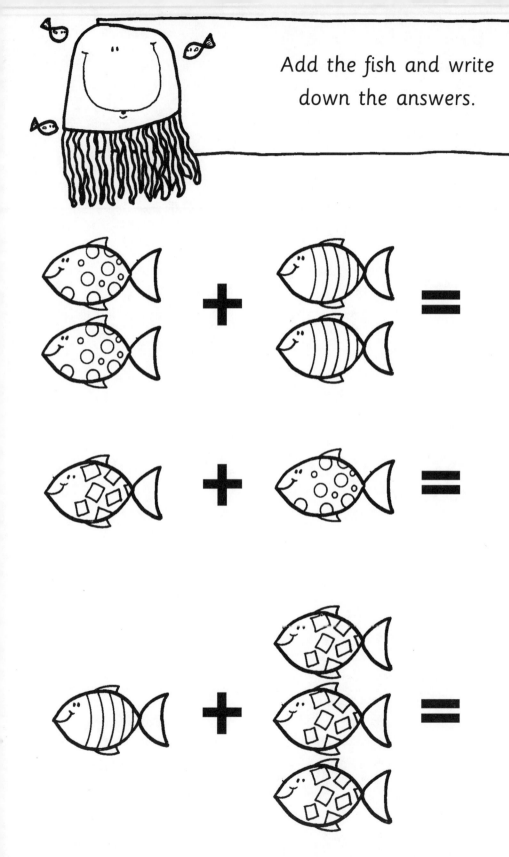

Write in the number
that is 1 more

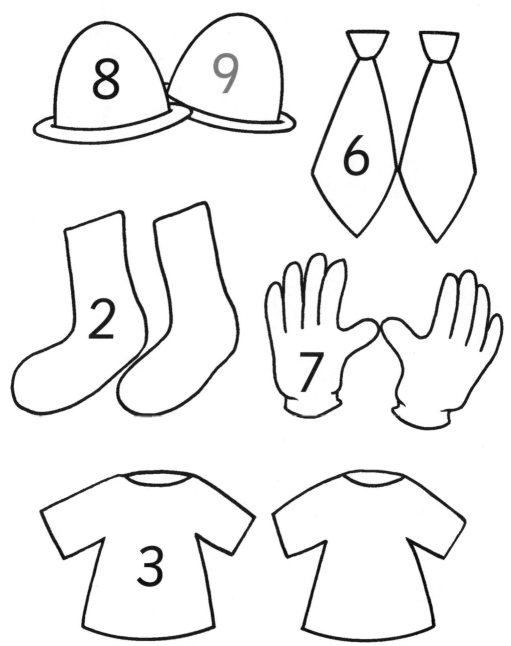

8 9

6

2

7

3

Draw lines from the words
to the right numbers.

one   two   three   four   five

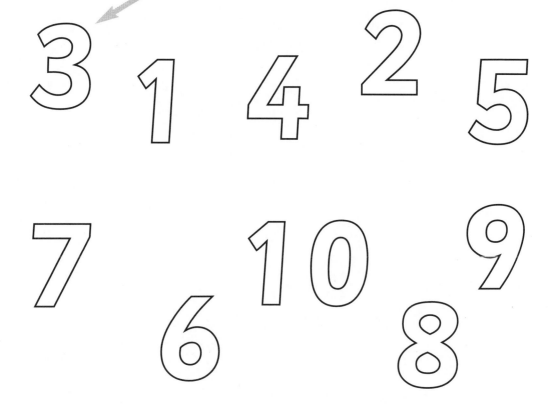

six   seven   eight   nine   ten

12

Colour in the pictures.
How many square(□)shapes
can you see in the pictures?

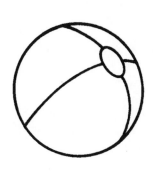 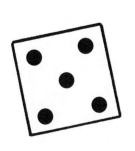 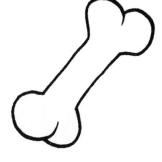

 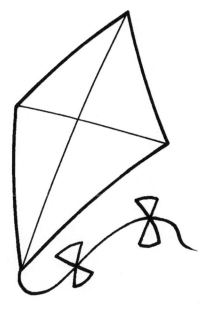

 squares

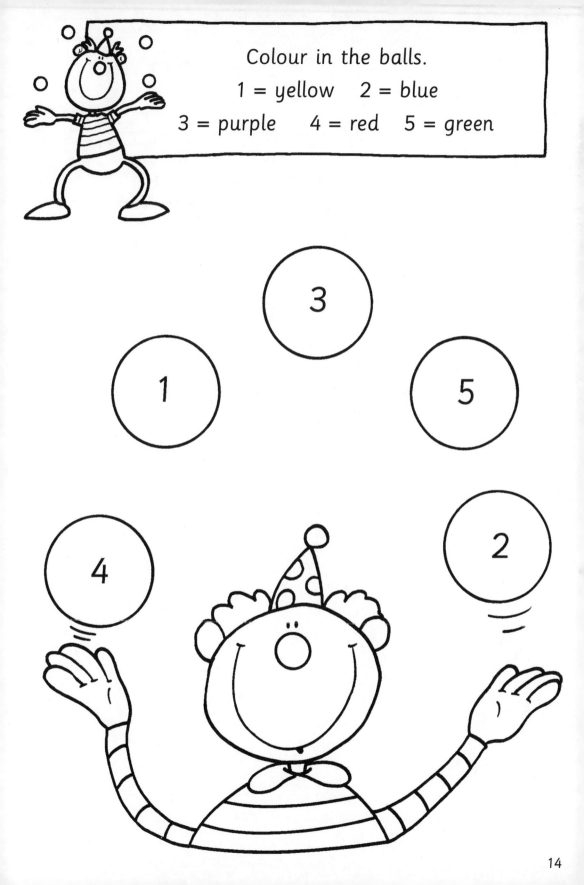

Colour in the balls.
1 = yellow   2 = blue
3 = purple   4 = red   5 = green

Join up the dots to find
who is in the picture.

4

7

5

6

3

8

2

9

1

10

Colour in the picture and count how many people there are on the school bus.

people

Follow the numbers in order
and help the frog find his
way across the pond.

What time is rabbit's bed time?

o'clock

How many mice are hiding
in the cheese?

mice

5 + 1=   3 + 2=

2 + 2=   6 + 1=

Colour in the pictures and
count the cats and dogs.

	cats		dogs

Colour in the pictures and
cross (✗) the odd one out.

Count and colour the
spots on the leopard.

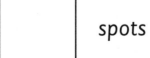
spots

Colour the coats of the
tallest children red and
the shortest children blue.

Colour in the pictures and count the different animals.

cats

dogs

rabbits

Add the sweets and write down the answers.

Which trail should the bear follow to get to the cake?

1

3

2

trail

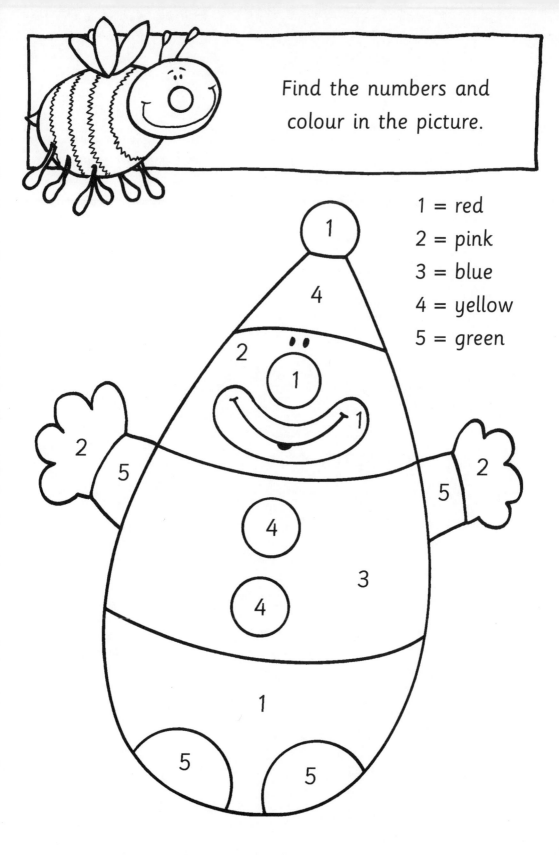

Find the numbers and colour in the picture.

1 = red
2 = pink
3 = blue
4 = yellow
5 = green

What time does the dog
go for a walk?

o'clock

Follow the path back to Earth by counting the planets.

1

3

2

4

5

6

7

8

10

9

Add the numbers on the dice
and write down the answers.

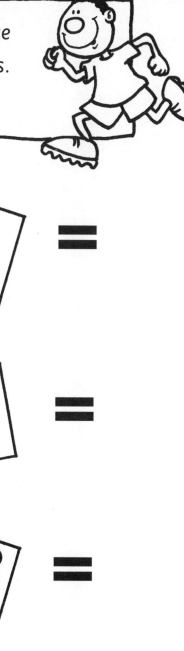

3 + 2 =

5 + 1 =

2 + 6 =

1 + 4 =

Help the pig eat all the
apples in the right order.

1

2

4

3

5

7

6

8

9

10

Count and colour the
spots on the ladybird.

spots

Which trail should the car take to the garage?

1

2

3

trail

Count and colour the buttons on the clown's costume.

buttons

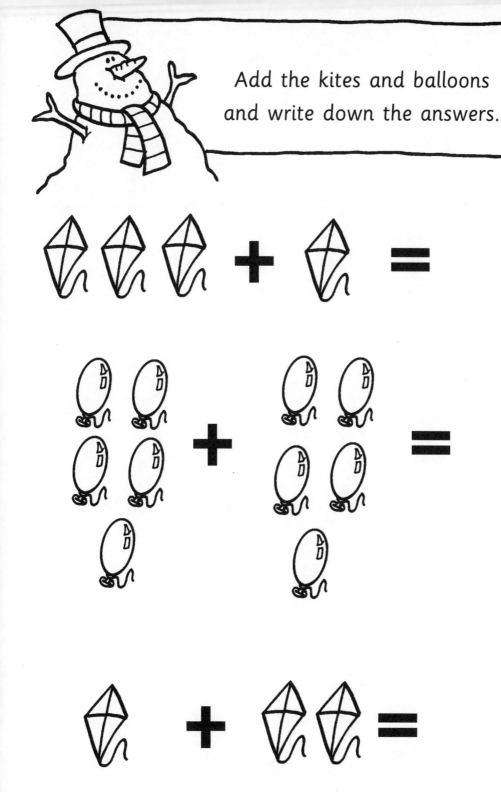

Add the kites and balloons
and write down the answers.

Take away the frogs and
write down the answer.

 frogs

 hop away

 frogs are left.

How many penguins are there?
Colour in the picture.

Four little penguins playing in the snow
Four little penguins want to say hello
Four little penguins what can they do?
Four little penguins are waving at you

penguins

Deliver the newspapers
in the right order.

2°

1°

5°

4°

3°

7°

6°

10°

9°

8°

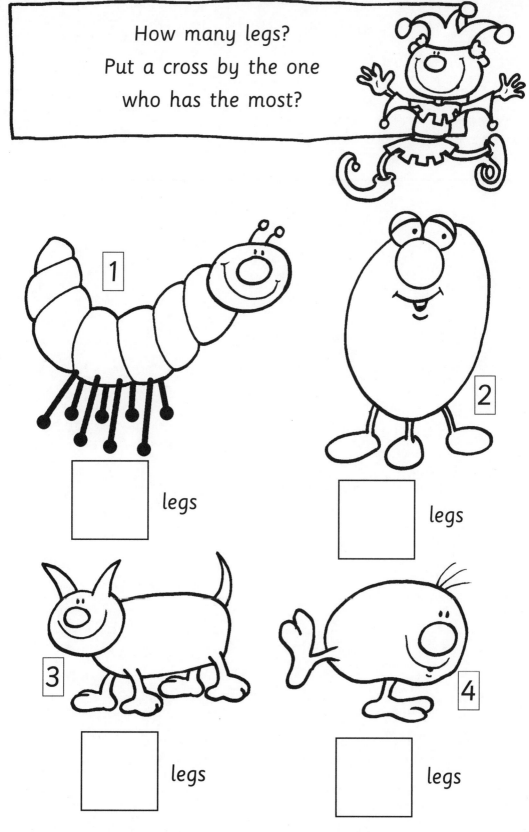

How many legs?
Put a cross by the one
who has the most?

1

legs

2

legs

3

legs

4

legs

40

Join up the dots to find
what is in the picture.

Colour 2 balloons yellow, 3 balloons green and 1 balloon red.
How many balloons?

balloons

Follow the numbers in order and help the clown find the way to his car.

What time does elephant
have her bath?

o'clock

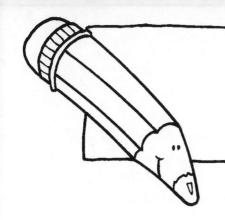

Join up the dots to find
who is in the picture.

5

4

6

7 8

3

2

9

1

10

Add the birds and the bees
and write down the answers.

3 + 1 =

2 + 2 =

4 + 1 =

Take away the birds and
write down the answer.

☐ birds

☐ fly away

☐ birds are left.

Colour and count the ice creams.
Follow the trails to
the right numbers.

3   8   1

Help the mouse to get
to the cheese.
How many cats does he pass?

cats

Colour in the pictures and count the giraffes and lions.

giraffes

lions

51

Colour 2 elephants red,
2 elephants blue and
2 elephants yellow.
How many elephants?

elephants

Colour in the pictures and count
the monkeys and parrots.

monkeys

parrots

Add the ducks and the frogs
and write down the answers.

 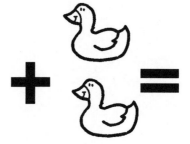

Count and colour the stars.

stars

Join up the dots to find who is in the picture.

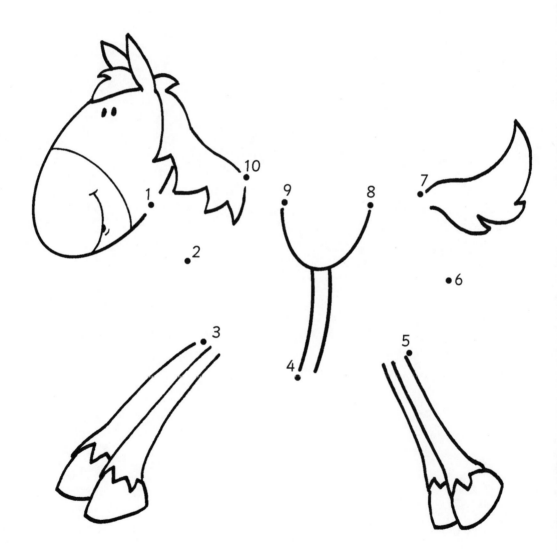

What time does it say on
the town hall clock?

o'clock

Colour in the pictures and cross (✘) the odd one out.

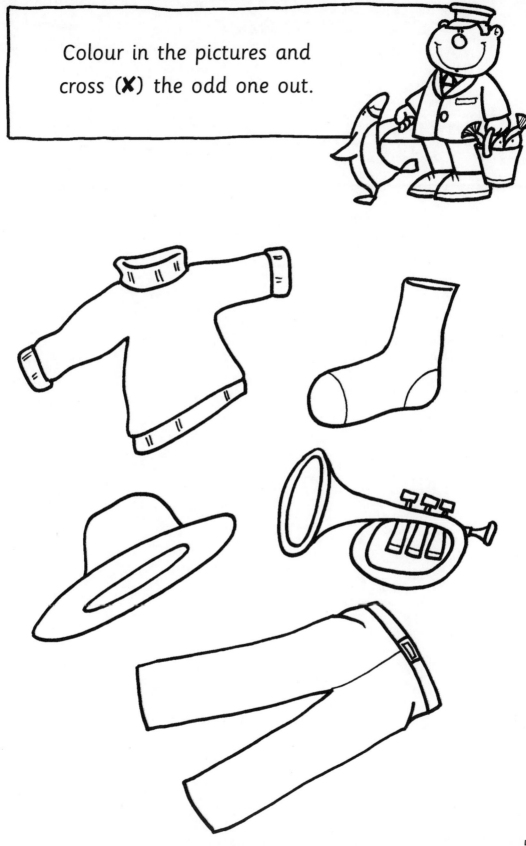

Colour the dogs with 3 spots yellow,
4 spots green and 5 spots red
How many dogs have 3 spots?

dogs have 3 spots

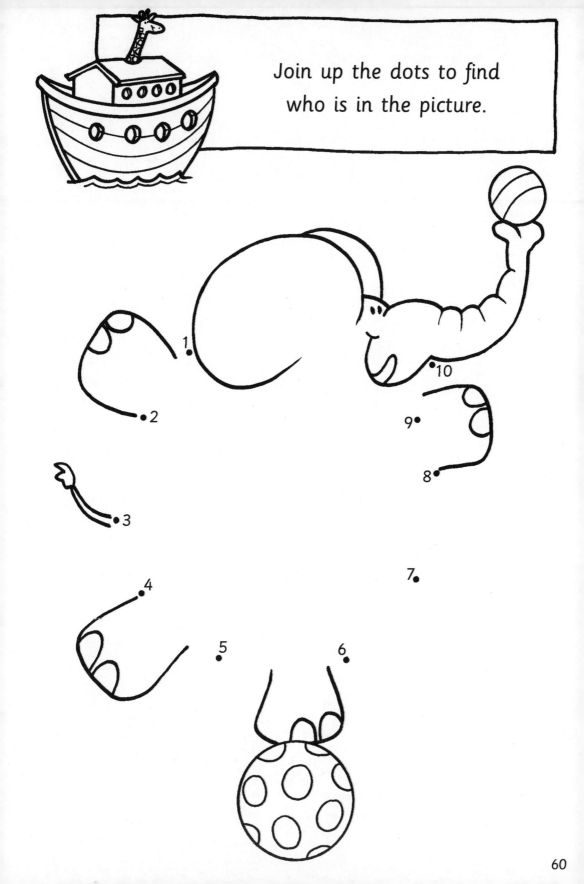

Join up the dots to find
who is in the picture.

60

Colour in the pictures and cross (**X**) the odd one out.

Help the rabbit to
get to the carrot.
How many flowers does she pass?

flowers

Colour in the pictures and count the cows, sheep and chickens.

cows

chickens

sheep

flags

Help the train get to the station.
How many trees does it pass?

trees

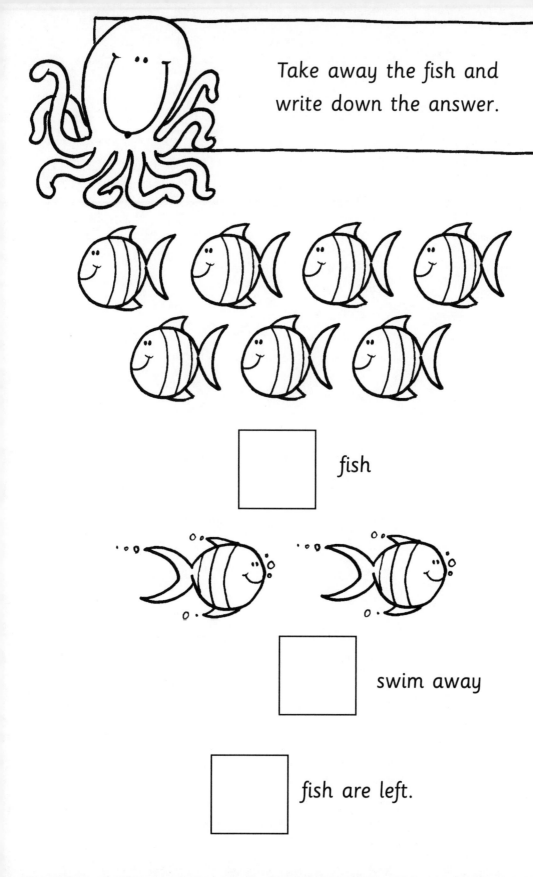

Take away the fish and
write down the answer.

☐ fish

☐ swim away

☐ fish are left.

66

Join up the dots to find
who is in the picture.

Colour 1 bear green, 3 bears
blue and 4 bears yellow.
How many bears?

bears

Colour the tallest
buildings green.

Colour 4 rocking horses red,
3 blue and 2 yellow.
How many horses are there?

rocking horses

Join up the dots to find
what is in the picture.

3
•

2
•

•
4

•
1

•
5

71

Colour in the pictures and count the different sea creatures.

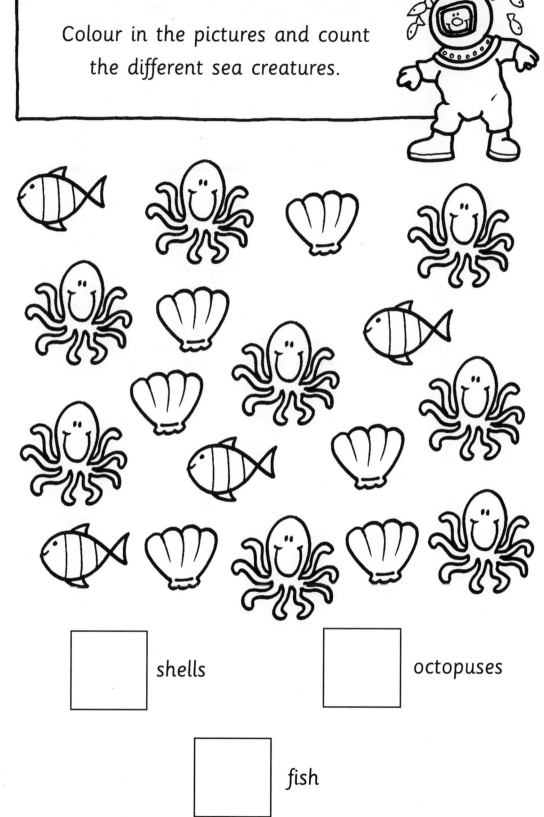

☐ shells

☐ octopuses

☐ fish

Take away the bananas and
write down the answer.

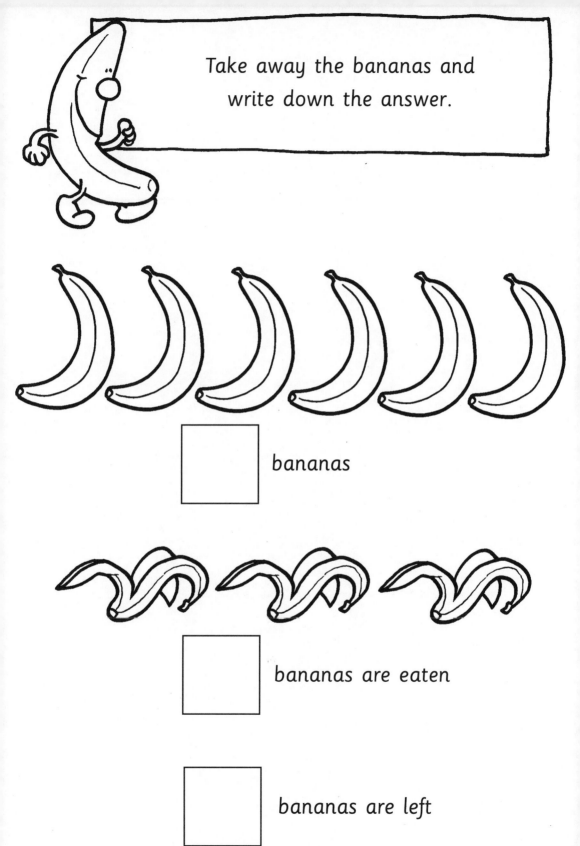

☐ bananas

☐ bananas are eaten

☐ bananas are left

Add the rabbits
and the carrots and write
down the answers.

+   =

+   =

+   =

Colour in the objects and count them. Write your answers in the boxes.

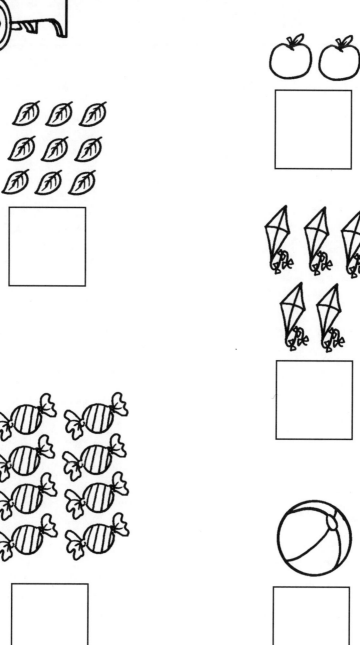

Write how many pigs
there are in the box and
colour in the picture.

Down in the farmyard a small pig on the run
Off to a party to have lots of fun
One pink pig has a birthday today
So all piggy's friends have come out to play

pigs

Write how many puppies
there are in the box and
colour in the picture.

Out in the garden it's a sunny day
Three little puppies have been out to play
Now it's all quiet, so tip-toe and peep
Tired little puppies all fast asleep

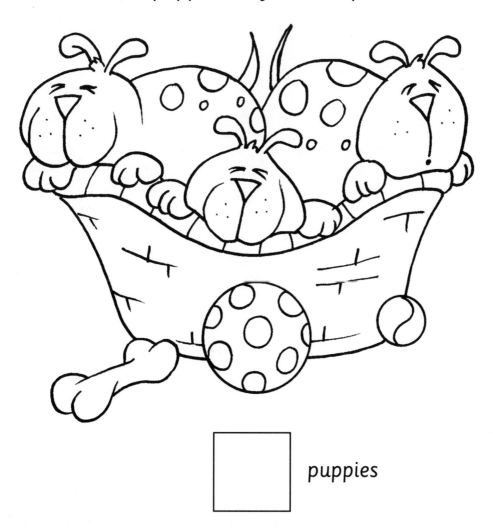

puppies

Follow the trails.
Which trail leads the boy
to his shoes?

1

3

2

trail

Colour 2 rabbits blue,
2 rabbits red and
3 rabbits yellow.
How many rabbits are there?

rabbits

Help the plane to land.
How many clouds does it pass?

clouds

Help the boat to get home.
How many fish does it pass?

fish

Take away the balloons and write down the answer.

☐ balloons

☐ are burst

☐ balloons are left

Colour 2 chickens red, 4 chickens yellow and 1 chicken blue.
How many chickens are there?

chickens

83

Colour the longest snake blue and green and the shortest snake red and yellow.

Colour and count the flowers and follow the trails to the right numbers.

7

4

3

Colour and count the balls and follow the trails to the right numbers.

5

3

6

Colour in the objects and count them. Write your answers in the boxes.

Take away the bones and
write down the answer.

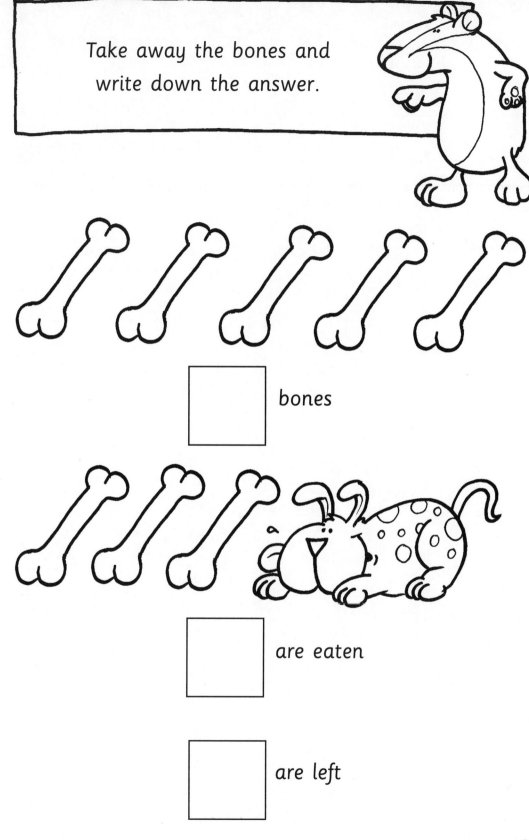

☐ bones

☐ are eaten

☐ are left

89

Take away the cakes and write down how many are left.

cakes

is eaten

cakes are left

Colour the shapes and count them.
Triangles = blue. Squares = red.
Circles = green. Stars = yellow.

☐ Squares   ☐   △ Triangles   ☐

☆ Stars   ☐   ○ Circles   ☐

Colour kite 1 red, kite 2 yellow,
kite 3 blue and kite 4 green.

answers

answers

25 Count the animals
5 cats   3 dogs   7 rabbits

26 Add the sweets
5, 9, 6, 4

27 Which trail?
number 1

29 What time is it?
5 o'clock

30 Follow the path to Earth
1-2-3-4-5-6-7-8-9-10

31 Add the numbers on the dice
5, 6, 8, 5

32 Eat the apples in order
1-2-3-4-5-6-7-8-9-10

33 Count the spots
7 spots

34 Which trail?
number 3

35 Count the buttons
6 buttons

36 Add the kites and balloons
4, 10, 3

37 Take away the frogs
4 - 2 = 2

38 How many penguins?
4 penguins

39 Deliver the newspapers
1-2-3-4-5-6-7-8-9-10

40 How many legs? Who has the most legs?
8, 3, 4, 2
Number 1 has the most - 8 legs

41 Join-the-dots picture
A train

42 How many balloons?
6 balloons

44 Help the clown
1-2-3-4-5-6-7-8-9-10

45 What time is it?
7 o'clock

46 Join-the-dots picture
A bird

answers

47 Add the birds and bees
5, 4, 5

48 Take away the birds
10 - 3 = 7

49 Count and follow the trails
8, 1, 3

50 Mouse maze
4 cats

51 Count the giraffes and lions
4 giraffes 5 lions

52 How many elephants?
6 elephants

53 Count the monkeys and parrots
4 monkeys   5 parrots

54 Add the ducks and frogs
8, 7, 5

55 Count the stars
10 stars

56 Join-the-dots picture
A horse

57 What time is it?
3 o'clock

58 Odd one out
The trumpet is the odd one out.
The rest are items of clothing.

59 How many dogs have 3 spots?
2 dogs

60 Join-the-dots picture
An elephant

61 Odd one out
The ladder is the odd one out.
The rest are pieces of furniture.

62 How many flowers?
6 flowers

63 Count the animals
3 cows   6 sheep   8 chickens

64 Count the flags
3 flags

65 How many trees?
4 trees

66 Take away the fish
7 - 2 = 5

67 Join-the-dots picture
A dog

answers

68	**How many bears?**	**79**	**How many rabbits?**
	8 bears		7 rabbits

68 How many bears?
8 bears

70 How many rocking horses?
9 horses

71 Join-the-dots picture
A house

72 Count the sea creatures
6 shells   8 octopuses   4 fish

73 How many bananas?
6 - 3 = 3

74 Add the rabbits and carrots
10, 7, 9

75 Count the objects
2, 9, 5, 8, 1

76 How many pigs?
4 pigs

77 How many puppies?
3 puppies

78 Which trail?
Number 3

79 How many rabbits?
7 rabbits

80 How many clouds?
6 clouds

81 How many fish?
5 fish

82 How many balloons?
5 - 3 = 2

83 How many chickens?
7 chickens

86 Count the flowers
3, 7, 4

87 Count the balls
6, 3, 5

88 Count the objects
7, 4, 3, 6, 10

89 How many bones?
5 - 3 = 2

90 How many cakes?
8 - 1 = 7

91 Count the shapes
6 triangles   3 squares
4 circles   5 stars